Peanuts and pollen!

The ACE project
'Literacy for Active Citizenship' series

Written by Ilham Sadi and Rose Ades
Illustrations by Sally Hancox

Peanuts and pollen!
© Learning Unlimited 2014

Published by Learning Unlimited Ltd as part of the Active Citizenship and Literacy (ACE) project. The ACE project, led by Learning Unlimited, was funded through the European Integration Fund and delivered in partnership with Blackfriars Settlement, Working Men's College and the Institute of Education.

Foreword

The ACE project
'Literacy for Active Citizenship' series

The Active Citizenship and English (ACE) project, led by Learning Unlimited and delivered in partnership with Blackfriars Settlement, Working Men's College and the Institute of Education, received funding from the European Integration Fund (July 2013 to June 2015).

The ACE project aimed to support non-EU women to develop their skills and confidence in English as well as the knowledge and confidence to take an active part in everyday life in the UK. As part of the project we wanted to produce a series of readers for our learners, and other adults also settling in the UK, which include stories about funny, personal and less typical aspects of everyday life in the UK. These books were written by learners and volunteers on the ACE project and the supporting activities have been developed by the Learning Unlimited team.

We hope you enjoy using the 'Literacy for Active Citizenship' series.

To find out more about the ACE project, please see:
www.learningunlimited.co/projects/ace

My name is Clara. Last year I came to live with my husband in London.

My husband is English. He has a friend called Alex. Soon after I arrived, Alex and his wife Zara invited us to a party.

At first I didn't want to go to the party because I spoke very little English.
I didn't know the culture.

My husband said Alex was kind. He said I would meet other nice people.

Oh! Everything was so new, different and unfamiliar. I had so many questions. What should I take? Flowers? Fruit? Chocolates? I could bake a cake - but maybe not?

A long time ago I made a lovely cake, full of fruit and nuts. I took it to a party. The next day the police came to our house. They asked me what was in the cake. A man had collapsed and hit his head. They said he'd been "stuffing himself" on my cake!

Thank goodness he got better. But I didn't want another cake casualty. Peanuts seem to be a big problem here in the UK too.

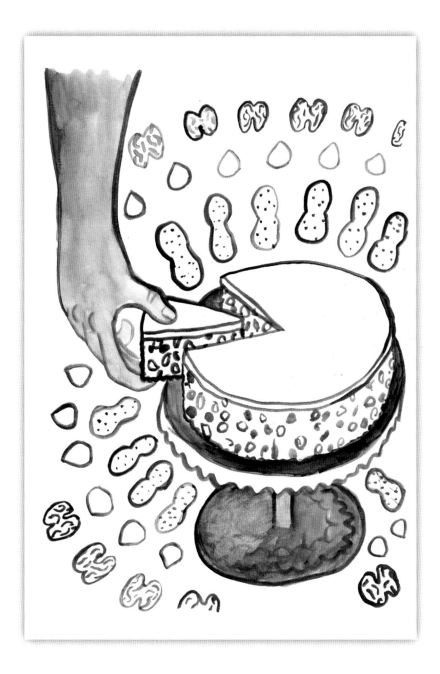

I decided to take some flowers to the party. Lilies are lovely and they sell them at the station. I decided to buy some on the way.

It was fun getting ready for the party.

When we arrived, I gave Zara the flowers. "Thank you so much. How kind of you. I love lilies. But I never buy them myself. These look pollen-free … Oh no! The pollen has come off on your dress."

I looked down in horror - and then I started to laugh.

My dress was covered in brown pollen.

The party was interesting even though I couldn't understand everything.

I even met someone who enjoys tongue twisters. She taught me a new one: *A proper copper coffee pot.*

It was fun!

Key words

casualty	person who has had an accident
collapse	become very ill and lose consciousness
culture	traditions from a country
lilies	a kind of flower with lots of brown pollen
pollen	a powder in the middle of flowers
recover	get better
stuffing	eating very quickly and greedily
tongue-twisters	words that are difficult to say together, for example: *Peter Piper picked a peck of pickled pepper*
unfamiliar	new and different

Questions

1. Who had the party?

2. What did Clara take to the party?

3. What happened at the party?

4. In your country, if you are invited to a party do you take a gift with you? If so, what do you take?

5. Can you say these tongue twisters?

   Red lorry. Yellow lorry.
   Red lorry. Yellow lorry.

   She sells seashells on the seashore.
   The shells she sells are seashells, I'm sure.

6. Do you know any tongue twisters in your own language? Say them to other students and explain what they mean.

Activities

Your dream dinner party

In small groups, tell each other who you would invite to your dream dinner party. It could be anyone at all! You could invite family members, friends, famous people, or people from books or history. For example, you could choose your best friend, your great-great-grandmother, Harry Potter, Queen Victoria and Beyoncé!

Explain why you would invite each person, for example:

I would invite .... because ....

For more downloadable activities, visit:
www.learningunlimited.co/resources/publications

Acknowledgements

Peanuts and pollen! was written by Ilham Sadi and Rose Ades and illustrated by Sally Hancox. We are grateful to them for being able to include their work as part of the 'Literacy for Active Citizenship' series.

To find out more about Learning Unlimited, its resources and published materials, CPD and teacher training programmes, project and consultancy work, please see: **www.learningunlimited.co**